JAMIE SMART'S
BUNNY vs MONKEY
RISE OF THE MANIACAL BADGER

6

I'M TIRED OF BEING STUPID.

IT'S TIME FOR ME TO DROP THE ACT, AND LIVE OUT MY DESTINY..

BZZ ZAP!

...AS THE GREATEST PIG SECRET AGENT THE WORLD HAS EVER SEEN!

THAT'S SO WEIRD, I HAD A DREAM ONCE THAT YOU WERE...

EAT POCKET HAND-WARMER, SNOW-BOT!

THIS ALL FEELS VERY STRANGE. A TIMER ON THE COCOONINATOR, SKUNKY FINALLY HAVING A GOOD IDEA, PIG A SECRET AGENT.

IT'S ALL JUST A BIT TOO SURREAL. ALMOST AS IF I'M...

7

9

11

14

AND I'M USING ALL MY MONEY TO FLATTEN YOUR WOODS, SO I CAN BUILD MY OWN WORLD!

BADGERTOPIA PLANS —

BADGERTOPIA!!

THIS MUST BE ANOTHER BAD DREAM. SOMEONE PINCH ME.

ME ME ME! PINCHY PINCHY!

SKUNKY! I NEVER THOUGHT I'D SAY THIS, BUT YOU NEED TO GET TO YOUR LABORATORY! BUILD SOMETHING TO **STOP** THE MANIACAL BADGER!

PINCH PINCH!

SIGH. WHAT'S THE POINT?

IT'S MY FAULT WE ALL GOT LOCKED IN STASIS, AND HE BECAME THE BEST SUPERVILLAIN IN THE WOODS.

MAYBE WE SHOULD JUST ACCEPT OUR FATE.

17

19

20

21

"DISTRACTION!"

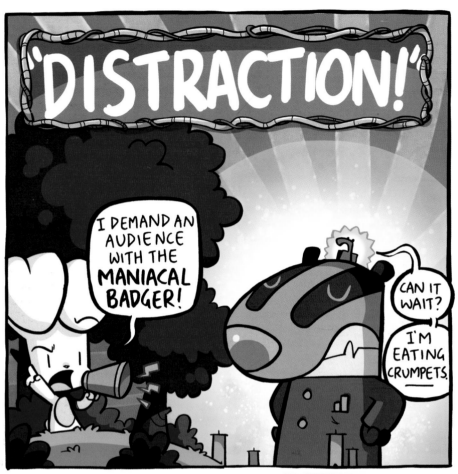

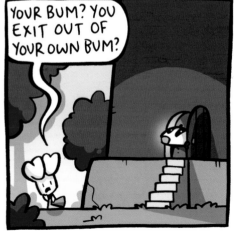

26

27

NO! EUGH! YOU SMELL LIKE THE TOILET!

JUST FOR A BIT. IT LOOKS COMFY.

SIGH.

SINCE THE MANIACAL BADGER HAS TAKEN OVER THE WOODS, I'VE FELT A BIT... USELESS.

HE'S ACHIEVED WHAT I NEVER COULD.

I'M A RUBBISH EVIL GENIUS.

WHAT'S THE POINT IN EVEN TRYING?

DON'T BE SO SILLY, SKUNKY. YOU'RE **VERY** GOOD AT BEING CRUEL AND RUTHLESS, AND EVERYONE SAYS SO.

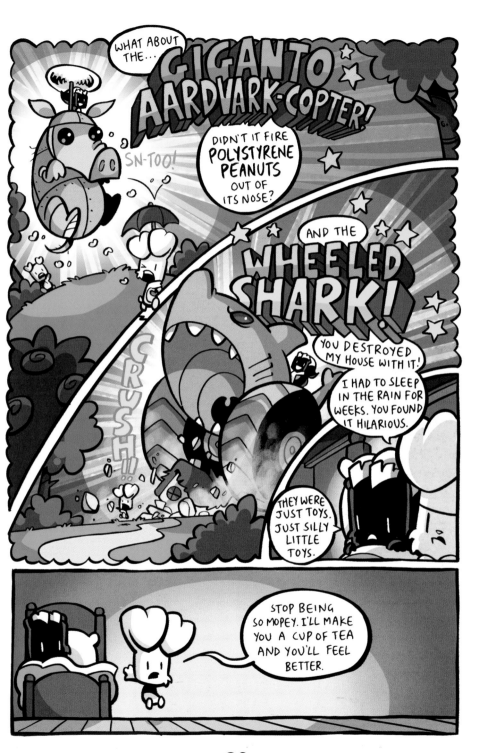

WHAT ABOUT THE...

GIGANTO AARDVARK-COPTER!

SN-TOO!

DIDN'T IT FIRE POLYSTYRENE PEANUTS OUT OF ITS NOSE?

AND THE

WHEELED SHARK!

CRUSH!

YOU DESTROYED MY HOUSE WITH IT! I HAD TO SLEEP IN THE RAIN FOR WEEKS. YOU FOUND IT HILARIOUS.

THEY WERE JUST TOYS. JUST SILLY LITTLE TOYS.

STOP BEING SO MOPEY. I'LL MAKE YOU A CUP OF TEA AND YOU'LL FEEL BETTER.

29

THANK YOU.

"MECHA SKUNKY!"

RUMBLE! RUMBLE! RUMBLE! RUMBLE! RUMBLE! RUMBLE!

SKUNKY! SKUNKY'S COMING!

AARGH!

WHAT DO YOU MEAN? SKUNKY HAS BEEN IN MY BED FOR THE LAST FOUR DAYS, EATING CRISPS, CRYING AND FARTING.

NOPE, IT WAS DEFINITELY SKUNKY!

TALLER THAN THE TREES, FIRING LASERS FROM HIS EYES!

METAL.

I DON'T REMEMBER HIM LOOKING LIKE THAT.

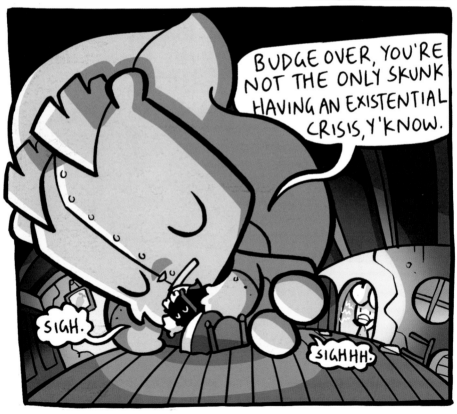

"ACTION BEAVER!"

WHO'S THAT CRAZY FOOL SPEEDING THROUGH THE TREES...?

HE'S THE DUDE WHO BREAKS ALL THE RULES.

HEY! HEYY! STOP THE SONG!!

I'VE FILLED 30 BALLOONS WITH ANGRY BEES!

I WANNA HELP ME CHUCK THEM AROUND?

BUZZ! BZZ! BUZZ!

HE ALWAYS STOPS TO HELP OUT FOOLS..

NOT AT US! NOT AT US!

BZZ!

BUZZ!

FLING! FLING! FLIN

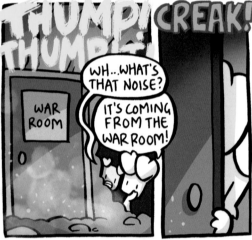

... COMPARED TO METAL STEVE'S DRILLING!

THIS ISN'T FAIR! WE CAME DOWN HERE TO GET AWAY FROM NOISE AND CALAMITY!

CRUMMBLE!

YEARGH!

BZZT! OOPS!

I LANDED ON MY BUM!

I LANDED ON PIG'S BUM TOO!

WHAT IS THIS PLACE?

I THINK I KNOW.

CLICK!

NOTHING.

I TOLD YOU ALREADY, I'VE GIVEN UP ON BEING AN EVIL INVENTOR! THESE CONTRAPTIONS ARE NOTHING BUT TROUBLE.

GNASH GNASH

BUT WE **NEED** YOU TO BUILD SOMETHING, SKUNKY! SO WE CAN DEFEAT THE MANIACAL BADGER!

NOPE.

BOOP!

ANYONE WANT A HOT CHOCOLATE?

WELL, THEN, FINE. IF SKUNKY WON'T DO IT, MAYBE WE CAN TRY FOR OURSELVES.

EVERYONE! YOU HAVE ONE HOUR! USE WHATEVER PARTS YOU CAN FIND TO CONSTRUCT YOUR OWN DEVIOUS INVENTIONS!

WHOEVER BUILDS THE BEST WINS!

FOOOOOOOO

HSUOO

II FFFOUNDD AAA ROCKETTT PACKKKK!

OKAY, PIG HAS DIBS ON THE ROCKET PACK. EVERYONE ELSE, IN 3...2...1...

...INVENT!!

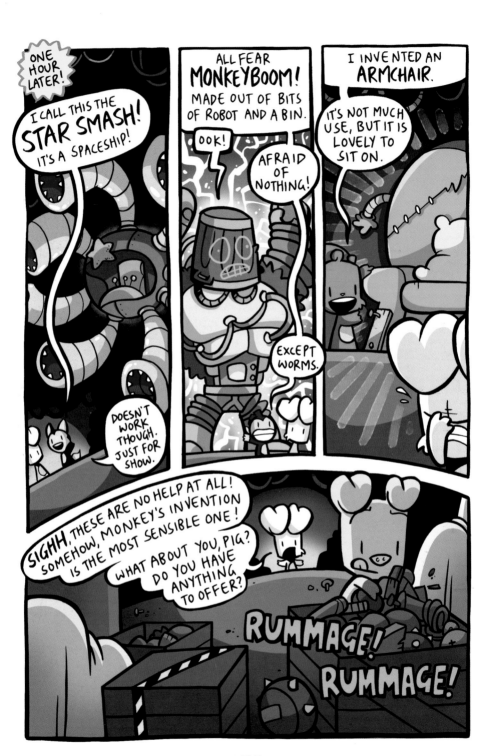

54

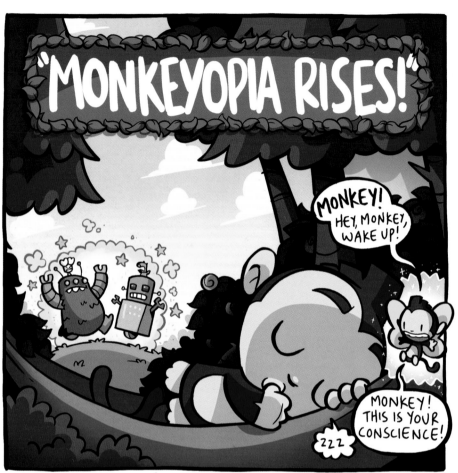

63

"ROFL-COPTER!"

SKUNKY'S SECRET LAIR FIRE ESCAPE (5 OF 39)

OUT OF BOUNDS -TO- BUNNIES

NOT THIS ONE TOO.

WHO'S BEEN BLOCKING OFF ALL THE ENTRANCES TO SKUNKY'S LAIR?

IT IS I, MONKEY, EMPEROR OF MONKEYOPIA!

MONKEY! I SHOULD HAVE KNOWN!

YOU CAN'T DO THIS! UNDER THE TERMS OF OUR TREATY, WE BOTH HAVE ACCESS TO SKUNKY'S INVENTIONS!

TREATY? HA! I SIGNED IT WITH MY BUM!

NO, YOU SIGNED IT WI...

OH, SO YOU DID.

ANYWAY, THE REASON I GET TO PLAY WITH ALL SKUNKY'S TOYS...

...IS BECAUSE SKUNKY IS **ON MY TEAM**! BROO HAR HARR!

HELLO.

SKUNKY, YOU REALLY SHOULDN'T BE INVOLVED IN ALL THIS. YOU'VE BEEN GOING THROUGH A VERY DIFFICULT TIME LATELY.

SIGH. NO, IT'S FINE.

IT **IS** FINE! WITH SKUNKY'S HELP, I'M GOING TO DEFEAT THE **MANIACAL BADGER**!

BOOP!

AND I'M GONNA DO IT IN...

...THE ROFL-COPTER!!

AND WHEN WE'RE DONE, I'LL BE COMING BACK FOR YOU!

THAT...THAT THING IS **HIDEOUS** YOU GOT SKUNKY TO BUILD IT?

NOPE! I BUILT IT MYSELF FROM BITS OF HIS OLD MACHINES.

BOOP!

INVENTING'S NOT HARD!

ROFL ROFL ROFL ROFL ROFL ROFL

SPUT! SPUT!

EUGH! IT SMELLS!

IT'S POWERED BY FARTS!

75

"TREASURE HUNT!"

80

I MADE HIM DO IT! ME! JUST BY PRESSING A BUTTON! MWAH HA HA!

THE MANIACAL BADGER!

WHILE YOU ALL SLEPT, I ACTIVATED THE **UNIVERSAL CONSOLE!**

I CAN NOW CONTROL THE WHOLE WOODS LIKE A HUGE VIDEO GAME!

THAT DOESN'T SOUND POSSIBLE.

WELL, IT IS. IT JUST... IS.

SOMEHOW.

LOOK IT JUST IS, OKAY?

ANYWAY, YOU'D BETTER PLAY NICE, BUNNY, BECAUSE IF THAT HEALTH METER ABOVE YOUR HEAD GETS TOO DAMAGED...

BADGER OTVO

...IT'S **GAME OVER!**

PFFT! I THINK I CAN KEEP MYSELF SAFE.

UM... BUNNY?

PRESS ⊗ TO LIGHT FUSE

I DON'T WANT TO DO THIS.

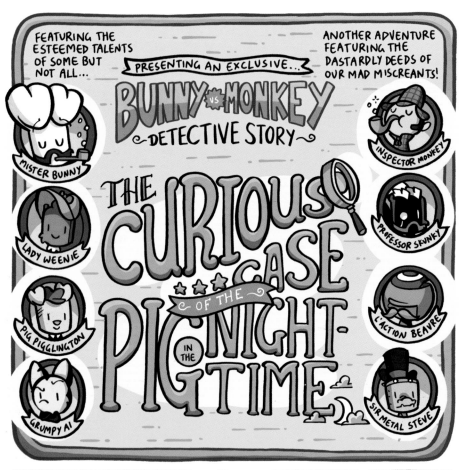

87

WHAT'S GOING ON? I HEARD AWOOGAS.

WE ARE THE ORDER OF THE MOOSE! WE HELP THOSE IN NEED!

OH. CAN I JOIN?

SORRY, BUNNY, BUT OUR SOCIETY IS SECRET! ONLY A SELECT FEW MAKE IT THROUGH THE INITIATION PROCESS.

ALL HAIL THE MOOSE!

WAIT, BUT THEY'RE ALL IN YOUR CLUB?

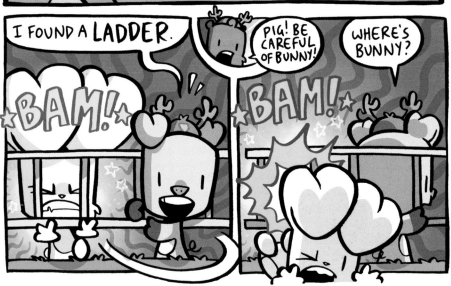

ANYWAY, WE CAN PUT THE LADDER AGAINST THE TREE, SO THE BIRD CAN CLIMB UP!

CLONK!!

YOU'RE ALL BEING RIDICULOUS! A **BIRD** CAN'T CLIMB A **LADDER!**

ALL YOUR ORDER HAS DONE SO FAR IS HIT ME IN THE FACE!

NO! THE ORDER OF THE MOOSE IS POWERFUL! ALL HAIL **THE MOOSE!**

AWOOGA! AWOOGA!

POWERFUL? YOU HAVEN'T HELPED THE BIRD AT ALL!

WHICH BIRD?

THE... BIRD!

WHERE'D THE BIRD GO?

HUMANS!!

TELL ME WHICH WAY THOSE FOOLISH CREATURES WENT, AND I WILL **SPARE YOUR LIVES!**

LOL. JUST JOKES, I WON'T.

BUT TELL ME ANYWAY!

WELL, SINCE YOU ASKED, TH... THEY...

NO! DON'T TELL HIM! HE'S JUST A BIG...MEAN... **PLOP NOSE!**

PLOP NOSE?!

I'LL HAVE YOU KNOW I'VE WON **BEST BADGER NOSE** IN THE ANNUAL BADGER NOSE CONTEST FOUR YEARS IN A ROW!

AND NOT JUST BECAUSE I IMPRISONED ALL THE OTHER CONTESTANTS.

I DON'T CARE. YOU'RE NOT HAVING METAL STEVE.

WHY CARE ABOUT **HIM?** HE DOESN'T CARE ABOUT **YOU!**

I FOUND SKUNKY'S OLD **MONSTER RAY!** TURNS ANY ANIMAL INTO A **SLOBBERING MONSTER VERSION OF ITSELF!** LIKE AN ANT. INTO A **MUT-ANT!**

THAT'S THE PREMISE ESTABLISHED!

WE WERE CALLING IT AN **ANT-A-SAURUS!**

WELL, MUT-ANT IS A BIT CLEVERER.

ANTHONY! THE BIG ANT!

HE'S THE PROTOTYPE FOR MY **MUT-ANT ARMY,** PRIMED TO CHOMP THE WORLD INTO **OBLIVION!**

DOES HE **LOOK** LIKE AN **ANTHONY?**

YES HE DOES, ACTUUUUALLY.

WELL, HE'S NOT.

HE'S A **TREVOR**, IF ANYTHING.

AND DON'T THINK I HAVEN'T SPOTTED YOU TRYING TO PINCH MY MONSTER RAY, BUNNY!

ZZONK!

OH HANG ON.

105

"THE MAKING OF A MANIACAL BADGER!"

GRAAAGH! ALL MY EVIL GENIUS, AND THOSE... ANIMALS STILL MANAGED TO DEFEAT MY LATEST INVENTION!

ARE YOU STILL WASTING YOUR TIME BUILDING THOSE SILLY TOYS?

THEY'RE NOT TOYS, FATHER!

SLURP!!

THEY'RE CRUEL INSTRUMENTS OF DESTRUCTION, DESIGNED TO TEAR THIS WORLD APART SO I CAN RULE IT TO MY MADDEST WHIMS!

I DON'T KNOW WHERE YOU GOT THIS ANGRY STREAK FROM. CERTAINLY NOT MY SIDE.

NOR MINE!

I KNOW JUST WHERE I GOT IT FROM...

114

WE WILL **FIX** IT!

YAYYYY! OH WAIT, HOW?

LUCKY FOR US, I ALWAYS CARRY MY **PICNIC BASKET 4000!**

KER-CHUNK! CHUNK!

IT CONTAINS SOMETHING FOR EVERY OCCASION!

A FEW MINUTES LATER...

HOW DOES THIS HELP?

SIGH.

YOU'LL NEED TO RECHARGE HIS POWER CORE. BY DIVERTING HIS, Y'KNOW, FLUXINATOR.

SKUNKY? WHAT ARE YOU DOING OUT HERE?

JUST ENJOYING THE UNTAMED BEAUTY OF NATURE, I GUESS.

SIGH.

HAR HARHAR! YOUR WEIRD MUDDY LUMP IS NO MATCH FOR THE TERRIFYING SUCTION...

VWOOP!

...OF THE HELLIPHANT!

THAT'S RIGHT, FLEE FOR YOUR LIVES!

THE HELLIPHANT WILL TEAR YOUR WOODS APART!

THAT LOOKS LIKE SOMETHING I INVENTED AGES AGO.

IT IS!

I STOLE YOUR PLANS AND I IMPROVED THEM!

SOUNDS LIKE A LOT OF EFFORT. WHY'D YOU DO THAT?

SIMPLE... TO CAPTURE YOU!

VWOOD

122

I SPENT **YEARS** TRYING TO HELP MONKEY TAKE OVER THE WOODS, BUT YOU STOLE MY INVENTIONS AND DID IT **OVERNIGHT!**

IT'S NOT FAIR!

IT'S NOT **FAIR!**

SLOP

SLIP!

IT'S NOT FAIR.

IT'S **PERFECTLY** FAIR! I OUT-SMARTED YOU! AND NOW I CAN JUST USE MY **BRAIN PROBE** TO TAKE WHATEVER EVIL GENIUS IS LEFT IN YOUR BRAIN!

FINE. DO IT. I DON'T CARE.

AHAHAHAA! HAAAAAA!

HEY, SKUNKY, WHY **DON'T** YOU FIGHT BACK?

SIGH.

126

127

WE DON'T KNOW.

HE NEVER CAME BACK.

WHAT? REALLY?

QUICKLY, WHILE HE'S PONDERING, INITIATE **OPERATION MUDSPOONS!**

WE CAN'T! **WE CAN'T!**

IT'S MIDSUMMER, SO THE MUD IS ALL **HARD** AND **CRACKED!**

DINK!

DINK! DINK!

WE CAN'T FLING IT!

YOU WERE ALL GOING TO... FLING MUD AT ME?!

NOW! DO IT **NOW!**

PAFFFF

HAHAHA! YOU FOOLISH CREATURES, YOU'RE **IDIOTS!** YOU CAN'T EVEN THROW **MUD** AT A **BADGER!**

YOU. ARE. **USELESS!**

THAT'S A BIT HARSH.

131

"A SHARP SHOCK"

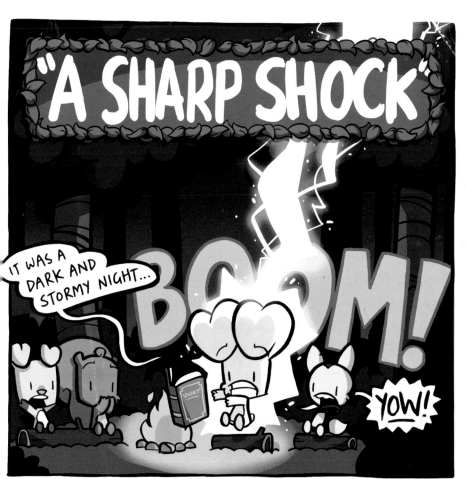

134

WE'RE **RUNNING AWAY!!**

OH! OH YES! **RUN AWAY! HAR HARRR!**

BUT HANG ON. IF YOU CREATED THAT MONSTER JUST BY BELIEVING IN IT.

THEN I... DON'T BELIEVE IN IT.

WHAT? DON'T BE SO **RIDICULOUS!**

LOOK! IT'S COUGHING UP LUMPS OF **RADIOACTIVE COAL!** YOU CAN **SEE** IT IS!

BLURG

NOPE! STILL DON'T...

OW!

...BELIEVE IT.

I DON'T EITHER! I DON'T BELIEVE IN IT!

BELIEVE IN WHAT?

EXACTLY! THERE'S NOTHING THERE!

NOW THE RAGNAGGTRIX IS ABOUT TO **EAT** YOUR PIGGY FRIEND! **NOW** YOU'LL BELIEVE IN IT!

141

"DISTRACTING THE MONKEY!"

SKUNKY! SKUNNNKKY! NOW YOU'RE INVENTING THINGS AGAIN, CAN YOU MAKE ME SOMETHING TO CAUSE RIDICULOUS **DAMAGE AND DESTRUCTION?**

FLOMP!

I WAS THINKING SOMETHING LIKE THIS! BUT, Y'KNOW, MORE **SCIENCEY**.

A giant banana

GO AWAY, MONKEY. I'M TOO BUSY TO BUILD YOUR SILLY IDEAS.

WHY? WHAT YOU DOING? WHATCHA WORKING ON?

N...**NOTHING!** DO **NOT** LOOK UNDER THIS TEA TOWEL. NO. **NO!**

HERE! YOU WANT TO SEE INVENTIONS? HERE'S AN INVENTION - THE **SPHERICAL CAT CANNON!**

OOOH. WHAT DOES IT DO?

BREAK◯GLASS

PRETTY MUCH WHAT IT SAYS.

PTOO! PT TOO!

MRAOW!

MRAOW!

MRAOW!

THIS IS **GREAT!**

BUT NOT QUIIIITE AS GREAT AS A... GIANT BANANA.

WELL... WHAT ABOUT...

...A MINIATURE ME?!

HELLO.

Ilmbulle Ilmuule

HE SAYS HE CAN BUILD YOU A GIANT BANANA.

OHHH.

MUCH TINY WORK LATER...

TAA DAA!

GRR!

OH.

NOPE. I WANT AN ACTUAL GIANT BANANA. AND I'M NOT LEAVING THIS UNDERGROUND LAIR UNTIL I HAVE ONE.

RRRGH...

144

148

...AAAND **THIS** IS MINE.

HMM, BUT I STILL HAVE ONE FLAG LEFT. WHAT ELSE CAN I CLAIM IN THE NAME OF MONKEYOPIA?

IS HE READY? IS HE READY?

I THINK HE IS! PRESENTING...

HMM.

152

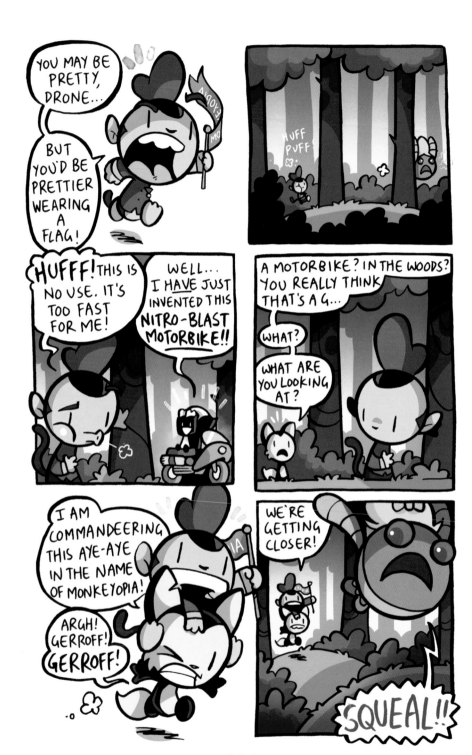

BUNNY VS MONKEY WARS
FINDS AND CAPTURES YOU ALL FROM THE REAL WORLD, AND FORCES YOU TO FIGHT!

DINK DINK!

OOH! I FOUND ONE!

THERE'S A **BUNNY** ROUND HERE.

YEAH, I KNOW.

BOOP BOOP!

BUNNIES ARE WORTH 75 POINTS.

I AM? OOH...

AAARGHHHH

I'D BETTER CAPTURE HIM QUICKLY!

ZWOOP!

WHAT HAVE YOU DONE WITH BUNNY?

BOOP BOOP!

COR! AN AYE-AYE TOO! I COULD DO WITH ONE OF THOSE.

OKAY, NOW WHAT?

NOW YOU FIGHT!

READY!

OKAY!

CLANGG!!

YOWWW! WHERE DID YOU GET A FRYING PAN FROM?!

THAT THING OVER THERE!

UPGRADES

THIS COULD BE A GAME CHANGER!

IT APPEARS WE CAN PURCHASE UPGRADES, USING IN-GAME TRANSACTIONS.

LEMME HAVE ANOTHER GO!

$

"BALLOONACY!"

162

THAT'S IT, DEREK! GO AND GET BARBARA FOR US!

HUH. THEY MUST HAVE HAD AN ARGUMENT.

NO MATTER! ALL OF BARBARA'S FRIENDS AND WORK COLLEAGUES ARE HERE TO HELP!

NOOO OOO!

PARTY BALLOONS

MANY HUFFS AND PUFFS LATER...

RIGHT! I'VE TIED EVERYONE AROUND MY TUMMY SO WE WON'T GET SEPARATED.

WEENIE? WHERE ARE YOU GOING?

164

I THINK THEY'VE **ALL** FALLEN OUT WITH BARBARA!

WHAT DID SHE **DO?**

OOH! I CAN SEE AI'S PARTY FROM HERE!

YAY!! YAY!

SORRY, BARBARA COULDN'T MAKE IT, AI. SHE'S BEEN HAVING A DIFFICULT TIME LATELY.

NOT AT ALL, PIG! IT'S NICE YOU BROUGHT SO MANY OTHER FRIENDS.

MORE CAKE?

W...WHAT? I MEAN, LOOK AT THE STATE OF YOUR BEDROOM! I'VE ALREADY HAD TO THROW OUT HALF OF YOUR JUNK!

WHAT?!

THANKS FOR THE...WHATEVER THIS IS, BADGER!

YOU BRING THAT BACK!

MOTHER, I AM A BRILLIANT MEGALOMANIAC! YOU CAN'T JUST...

IS HE GOING ON ABOUT BEING A BRILLIANT MEGALOMANIAC AGAIN?

YEP.

I AM GOING TO RULE THIS PLANET!

WELL, TIDY YOUR ROOM BEFORE YOU DO.

A NOISE ONLY FLIES CAN HEAR!

173

FATHER! NO!!

OH, LUMME HECK!

I'LL SWITCH IT OFF! I'LL SWITCH IT OFF!

TOO LATE FOR US, SON.

WE'RE ON OUR WAY TO HELL NOW.

OH, LUMME HECK TOO!

WHERE'S HELL?

SOMEWHERE OUTSIDE LONDON, I THINK.

I JUST SUCKED MY OWN PARENTS INTO HELL!

VTTTT!

NO! NOOO!

FIVE MINUTES LATER...

WAHOOOO!

HONK HONK!

174

181

...WITH A **BEAVER WITH A JETPACK!!**

WHERE DID ACTION BEAVER GET A JETPACK FROM?

SEE NOW, THAT DOESN'T REALLY MATTER.

WHAT MATTERS IS THAT WHEN YOU GIVE AN ALREADY EXCITABLE WOODLAND CREATURE THE TECHNOLOGY TO PROPEL HIMSELF THROUGH THE AIR AT HIGH SPEED, WHAT Y'ALL ARE LEFT WITH IS...

ARGH

OW!

SCREAM!

...**ABSOLUTE CHAOS!**

HOW DO WE GET HIM BACK DOWN?

I HAVE AN IDEA.

SKUNKY! MAKE US **ALL** JETPACKS!

AT LAST!

186

IT'S NO USE!

HE'S IMPOSSIBLE TO CATCH!

WELL, YOU MAY ASK, HOW DID THEY CATCH JETPACK BEAVER?

AND THE ANSWER IS...

188

"PIGGING RICH!"

WHAT HO! MY NAME IS PIGGENDEN PONSONBY SMYTHE, AND I AM THE RICHEST PIG IN THE WORLD!

PARP PARP!

WELL, I DIDN'T VOTE FOR YOU.

DAD, HE'S OUR WEALTHY UNCLE! YOU SHOULD BE MORE POLITE!

NAH, I'D RATHER ROLL AROUND IN SOME MUD.

189

UM...

PIG.

WHICH ONE OF US IS PIG?

ME? OH! IT'S ME!

WASN'T IT YOU?

WHY ARE YOU DRESSED IN A SILLY BONNET?

BECAUSE IT'S SILLY BONNET DAY! OBBBVIOUSLY.

TCHUH!

SIGHHH—THIS IS NO GOOD. NO GOOD AT ALL! I CAME OUT HERE TO FIND MY LAST LIVING RELATIVES, ONLY TO FIND OUT THEY'RE ALL **IDIOTS**!

WHICH IS A SHAME, AS I WAS HOPING TO INVEST MY **ENTIRE RIDICULOUS FORTUNE** INTO A PIG WORTHY OF IT.

MMMONEY?

192

197

WHEN YOU IDIOTS HAVE DESTROYED THESE WOODS AND TURNED THEM TO DUST, I WILL BE ROCKETING MYSELF TO THE MOON, THANK YOU VERY MUCH.

SORRYYY!

ONCE THERE, I'LL LOB THE ORB ONTO THE ROCKY SURFACE.

SMASH!!

AS SOON AS IT SHATTERS, THE SEEDS OF LIFE WILL ACTIVATE AND RAPIDLY SPREAD.

WITHIN SECONDS, THE WHOLE MOON WILL BE COVERED WITH LUSH, FERTILE GROUND.

PLO OOP!

A NEW HOME FOR CIVILISATION.

NAMELY ME.

TO BE HONEST, I'VE BEEN TOYING WITH THE IDEA OF DESTROYING PLANET EARTH JUST TO TRY IT...

HEY! WHERE DID MY ORB GO?

GONE!!

YOU WERE BEING BORING, SO I PUT IT ON MY HEAD.

NO! NOOOO!

WINTER

"A VERY BADGER CHRISTMAS" (PT. 1)

SNOWWWWWWWWWWWWWWW!

FLUMP!

IT CERTAINLY WAS A HEAVY SNOWFALL LAST NIGHT!

IT'S AMAAAAZING!!

I'VE ALREADY BUILT A SNOW STATUE OF **THEOI OURANIOI**, THE GREEK GODDESS OF WEATHER!

AND I'VE ALREADY DESTROYED IT! HA HA HAAA!

SPLPB!

MONKEY, DID YOU JUST CAUSE AN AVALANCHE?

I...DON'T THINK SO?

207

SAFE TO SAY, THIS'LL GO DOWN AS OUR WORST CHRISTMAS **EVER.**

AW- HEY, DON'T BE TOO DOWN-HEARTED.

...WE GOTS **CRACKERS!!**

YEAH.

THAT'LL HELP.

SNPP!

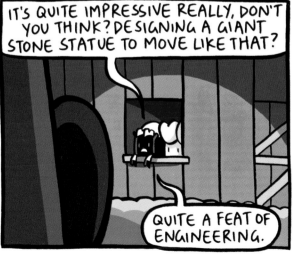

IT'S QUITE IMPRESSIVE REALLY, DON'T YOU THINK? DESIGNING A GIANT STONE STATUE TO MOVE LIKE THAT?

QUITE A FEAT OF ENGINEERING.

THANK YOU! AND DO YOU WANT TO KNOW HOW I DID IT?

219

221

"AFTERMATH"

THIS USED TO BE MY **LIVING ROOM.** I'D SIT HERE AND FALL ASLEEP IN A BOWL OF CARROTS.

THIS HAS BEEN THE WORST CHRISTMAS EVER.

BEST CHRISTMAS EVER! ONK! ONKKKK!

HOW CAN YOU SAY THAT? SKUNKY HAS TURNED OUR WOODS TO **DUST!**

IT WASN'T ME, IT WAS THE **MANIACAL BADGER!**

TEE HEE HEE!

228

HOW TO DRAW THE
MANIACAL
BADGER

① WE DRAW THE MANIACAL BADGER VERY DIFFERENTLY TO ALL THE OTHER BUNNY VS MONKEY CHARACTERS BECAUSE WE START WITH THE BODY FIRST! HIS BODY IS A **LUMP SHAPED LIKE THIS!**

TO THE BODY, WE ADD A DOLLOP SHAPE FOR HIS HEAD, LIKE THIS.

THEN WE CAN CONNECT IT TO HIS MOUTH. HERE WE'VE DRAWN SNARLING **TEETH!**

④ **EYES!** THE MANIACAL BADGER USUALLY HAS VERY ANGRY EYES, SO ADD THEM TO THE TOP OF HIS HEAD!

⑤ THEN ADD A GREAT BIG TRIANGLE FOR A **NOSE**, JUST AT THE END OF HIS SNOUT.

⑥ **EARS!** TWO LITTLE LUMPS AT THE VERY TOP OF HIS HEAD.

⑦ THEN WE NEED TO ADD A BADGER STRIPE UNDERNEATH EACH EYE.

⑧ DRAW IN THE TOP OF HIS **CLOAK!**

⑨ ADD SOME BUTTONS, AND A POCKET WITH PENS IN IT.

(10) FOR THE **ARMS**, AGAIN WE'LL USE A SAUSAGE SHAPE. THIS TIME LET'S DRAW HIM POINTING!

(11) SINCE THE MANIACAL BADGER'S CLOAK OFTEN COVERS HIS FEET, IT HELPS TO DRAW A LITTLE SHADOW UNDERNEATH HIM.

(12) LASTLY, LET'S MAKE SURE HE IS HAVING ANOTHER **DIABOLICAL IDEA** BY DRAWING IN A THOUGHT BUBBLE!

AND THERE WE HAVE THE **MANIACAL BADGER!** TRY USING ALL YOU'VE LEARNT TO DRAW HIM IN LOTS OF DIFFERENT POSES, LIKE THIS!

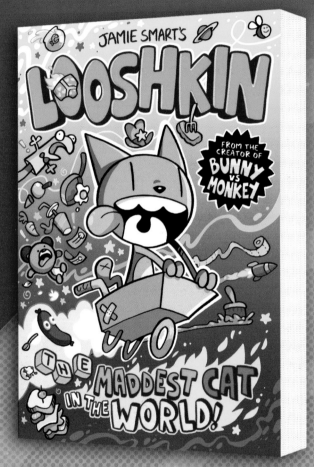

ENTER THE WORLD OF
JAMIE SMART'S

FLEMBER

DISCOVER THE MAGICAL POWER OF FLEMBER, WITH BOY-INVENTOR DEV, AND HIS BEST FRIEND BOJA THE BEAR!

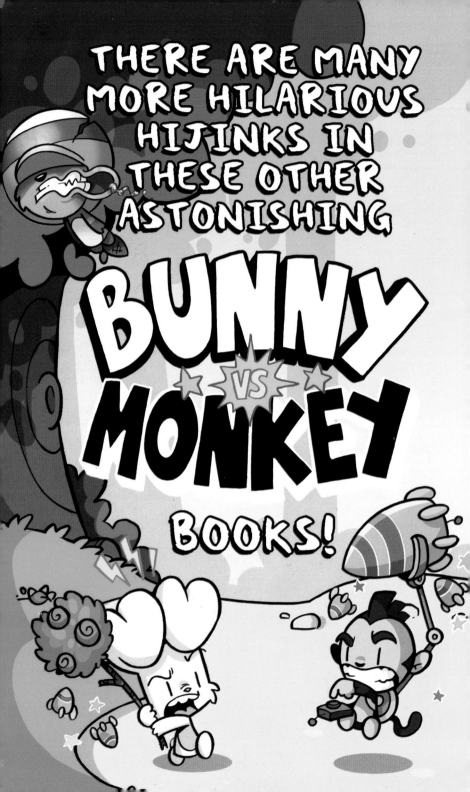

THERE ARE MANY MORE HILARIOUS HIJINKS IN THESE OTHER ASTONISHING

BUNNY VS MONKEY

BOOKS!

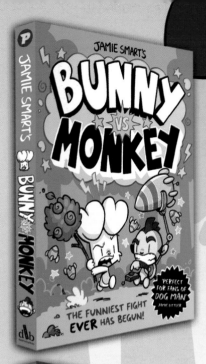

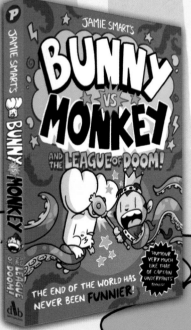

WITH MANY MORE
COMING SOON!

WWW.THEPHOENIXCOMIC.CO.UK

JAMIE SMART HAS BEEN CREATING CHILDREN'S COMICS FOR MANY YEARS, WITH POPULAR TITLES INCLUDING *BUNNY VS MONKEY*, *LOOSHKIN* AND *FISH-HEAD STEVE*, WHICH BECAME THE FIRST WORK OF ITS KIND TO BE SHORTLISTED FOR THE ROALD DAHL FUNNY PRIZE.

THE FIRST THREE BOOKS IN HIS *FLEMBER* SERIES OF ILLUSTRATED NOVELS ARE AVAILABLE NOW. HE ALSO WORKS ON MULTIMEDIA PROJECTS LIKE *FIND CHAFFY*.

JAMIE LIVES IN THE SOUTH-EAST OF ENGLAND, WHERE HE SPENDS HIS TIME THINKING UP STORIES AND GETTING LOST ON DOG WALKS.